DINOSAURS
COLORING BOOK

Pomegranate

PORTLAND, OREGON

Original artworks reproduced in this coloring book are by Ukrainian paleoartist Sergey Krasovskiy.
All photographs are courtesy Stocktrek Images, Inc. / Alamy Stock Photo.

1. An alvarezsaurid bird cleans the mouth of a *Giganotosaurus carolinii*
2. *Muttaburrasaurus langdoni* in a prehistoric environment
3. A raptor stalks a pair of grazing *Europasaurus holgeri*
4. *Pycnonemosaurus nevesi* run at the time of attack
5. A group of *Tapuiasaurus macedoi*
6. *Zhuchengtyrannus magnus* mother with offspring
7. A pair of *Erlikosaurus andrewsi*
8. *Amurosaurus riabinini* graze in wetlands
9. An *Albertosaurus* observes a family of *Arrhinoceratops*
10. An *Altispinax dunkeri* duo corrals a group of *Iguanodon*
11. A group of *Balaur bondoc*
12. Conflict between two male *Altirhinus kurzanovi* as females graze
13. *Mamenchisaurus sinocanadorum* feed on brown algae at low tide
14. Two *Kosmoceratops* stampede through a *Talos* nesting site
15. *Concavenator corcovatus* theropods circle each other while sauropods look on
16. A *Bakonydraco* pterosaur attacks a nest of *Ajkaceratops*
17. *Dilong paradoxus* in search of food
18. *Giraffatitan* and *Dicraeosaurus* sauropods grazing
19. A *Neovenator* allosaur looms over a *Polacanthus*
20. A meat-eating *Labocania* attacks a young plant-eating *Magnapaulia*
21. Two *Gigantspinosaurus* stegosaurs in sight of a large *Yangchuanosaurus* theropod
22. A *Saurolophus* hadrosaur rears up beside a *Tarchia* ankylosaur

. . . .

Color reproductions © 2019 Sergey Krasovskiy
Photographs courtesy Stocktrek Images, Inc. / Alamy Stock Photo
Line drawings © Pomegranate Communications, Inc.

ISBN 978-0-7649-8660-4
Item No. CB205

Designed by Sophie Aschwanden

Pomegranate Communications, Inc.
19018 NE Portal Way, Portland, OR 97230
800-227-1428   www.pomegranate.com

Pomegranate Europe
Number 3 Siskin Drive, Middlemarch Business Park
Coventry, CV3 4FJ, UK
+44 (0)24 7621 4461   sales@pomegranate.com

This product is in compliance with the CPSIA. A General Conformity Certificate and tracking information are available through Pomegranate.

Printed in Korea

28 27 26 25 24 23 22 21 20 19   10 9 8 7 6 5 4 3 2 1

DINOSAURS
COLORING BOOK

In this book, you'll find awesome dinosaur drawings to color, created from the work of Ukrainian artist Sergey Krasovskiy.

As a paleoartist (an artist who focuses on ancient fossil animals and plants), Krasovskiy depicts dinosaurs and pterosaurs—long extinct—in their prehistoric environments. Accuracy is important to the artist, and he often incorporates scientific discoveries when portraying these mysterious creatures. His paintings don't shy away from the realities of survival (check out the teeth on some of these guys!), yet they also picture peaceful moments in the everyday lives of dinosaurs from long ago.

Krasovskiy grew up in Donbass, Ukraine, and studied art at university in Lugansk. The artist has a large following as a freelance illustrator, and his work has been published on postage stamps and in magazines and books around the world. Reproductions of the original artworks are provided on the inside of the front and back covers. Information about these amazing creatures of the past is included on the facing pages of the line drawings to be colored.

Pomegranate

PORTLAND, OREGON

An alvarezsaurid bird cleans the mouth
of a **Giganotosaurus carolinii**

Among the largest known theropods, *Giganotosaurus carolinii* was likely an apex predator, with teeth up to eight inches long. Though its skull was about six feet long, its brain was likely the size and shape of a banana.

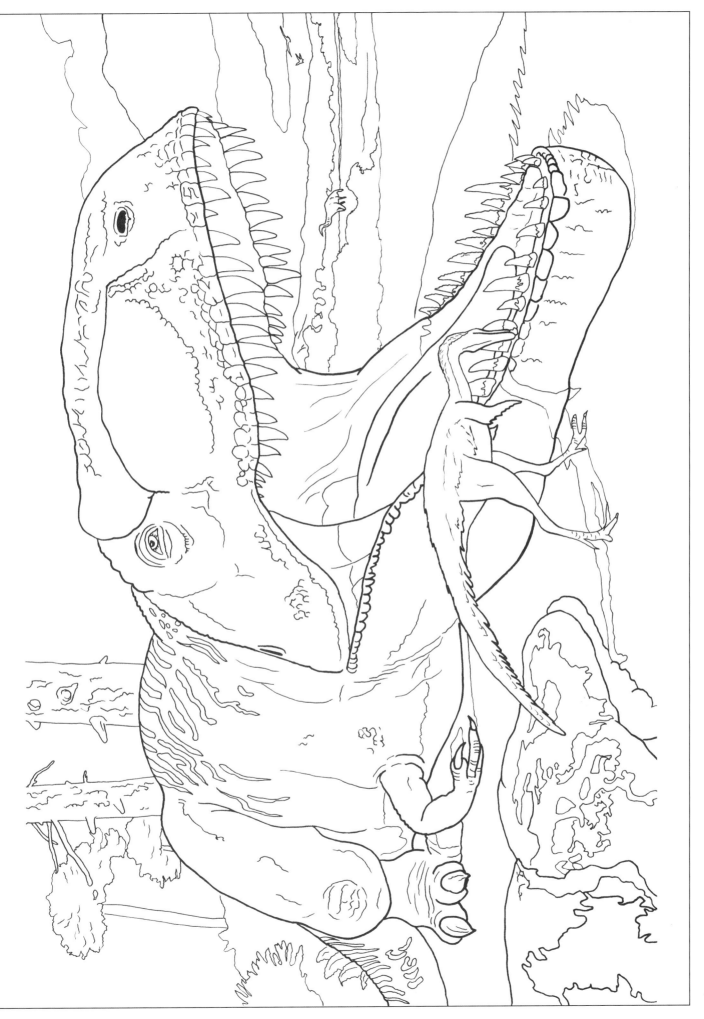

1

Muttaburrasaurus langdoni in a prehistoric environment

In 1963, near the Queensland, Australia, town of Muttaburra, a relatively complete dinosaur skeleton was discovered in a rocky area that was once a shallow sea. *Muttaburrasaurus langdoni*, however, was not aquatic. This Early Cretaceous herbivore is thought to have roamed about on two legs, perhaps standing tall to munch on understory vegetation.

2

A raptor stalks a pair of grazing **Europasaurus holgeri**

Though twenty feet long, *Europasaurus holgeri* is known for its dwarfism. Discovered in northern Germany, it likely lived on islands during the Late Jurassic period and became reduced in size (compared to similar dinosaurs) as a response to limited resources.

3

Pycnonemosaurus nevesi run at the time of attack

Carnivorous *Pycnonemosaurus nevesi* dinosaurs have been found in the Bauru Group of southwestern Brazil. This abelisaurid—from the Late Cretaceous epoch, likely the Campanian or Maastrichtian stage—is thought to have been approximately twenty-nine feet long.

4

A group of **Tapuiasaurus macedoi**

At an estimated forty feet long, *Tapuiasaurus macedoi* was small among titanosaurs, a group that includes the largest land animals known to have inhabited earth. This Early Cretaceous herbivore likely ate leaves that it pulled from trees.

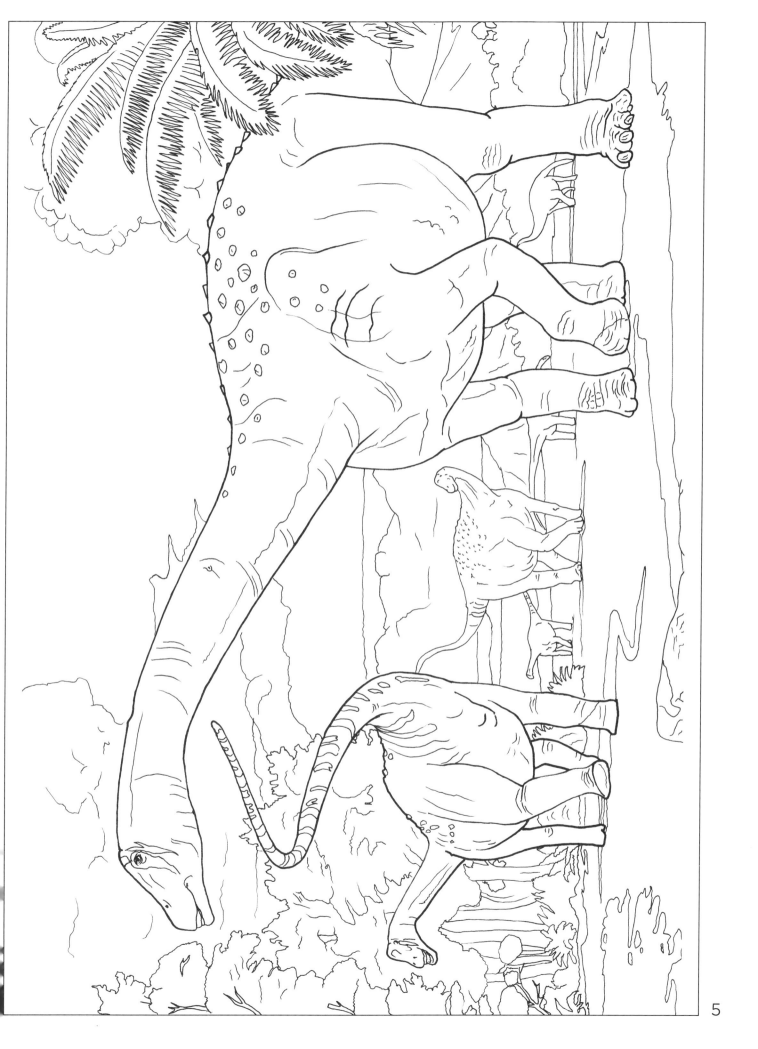

5

Zhuchengtyrannus magnus mother with offspring

Known so far only through jawbones of its holotype, found in eastern China, *Zhuchengtyrannus magnus* was certainly a giant. This carnivore was a relative of the well-known *Tyrannosaurus rex* and potentially weighed more than six tons.

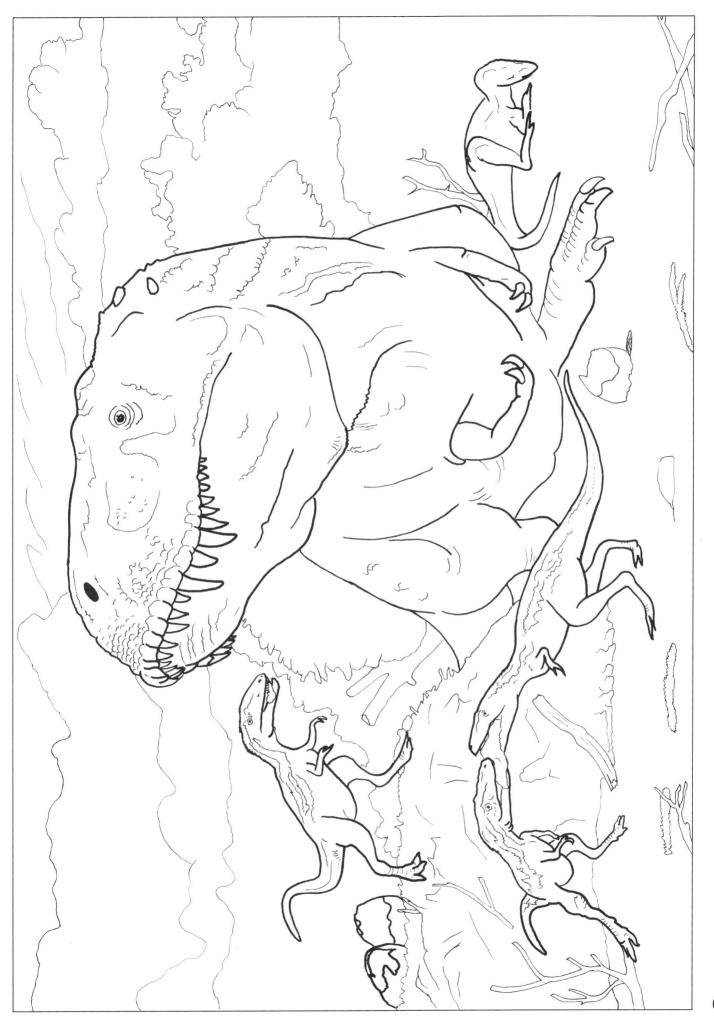

A pair of **Erlikosaurus andrewsi**

Discovered in Mongolia, *Erlikosaurus andrewsi* was a Late Cretaceous herbivorous theropod. It is suspected of having a keratinous beak, much like modern birds, in addition to having teeth.

Amurosaurus riabinini graze in wetlands

Amurosaurus riabinini, an herbivore of the Maastrichtian stage, was found in the Amur region of far eastern Russia. This duck-billed, hollow-crested hadrosaur is known through specimens from a single fossil-rich bone bed.

8

An **Albertosaurus** observes a family of **Arrhinoceratops**

Inhabiting marshes and forested floodplains in Canada, *Arrhinoceratops* lived during the Late Cretaceous epoch. Its name means "without nose-horn face," given despite the presence of a nose horn. This herbivore was prey to *Albertosaurus*.

10

A group of **Balaur bondoc**

Discovered in Romania, *Balaur bondoc* got its name from a dragon-like creature of local folklore. This theropod from the Maastrichtian stage was likely a flightless bird, six to seven feet long and about the size of a turkey or goose.

11

Conflict between two male **Altirhinus kurzanovi**
as females graze

Altirhinus kurzanovi, an ornithopod from the Early Cretaceous epoch, is recognizable for its high nasal arch, but it also had an interesting trait on its forefeet: the interior digit was a sharp spike.

12

Mamenchisaurus sinocanadorum
feed on brown algae at low tide

Mamenchisaurus sinocanadorum was among the largest dinosaurs, measuring approximately 115 feet—its neck alone stretched to around 55 feet. Found in China, this sauropod lived during the Late Jurassic epoch.

Two **Kosmoceratops** stampede through a **Talos** nesting site

Kosmoceratops, with fifteen horns and spikes on its head, has been called "the horny-est dinosaur ever." *Talos*, with a retractable sickle-shaped claw on its second toe, is known as a "switchblade-clawed predator." Remains of these dinosaurs were found within the Grand Staircase-Escalante National Monument in southern Utah, a hotbed of dinosaur diversity.

Concavenator corcovatus theropods circle
each other while sauropods look on

At nearly twenty feet long, *Concavenator corcovatus* is considered medium-sized among its Early Cretaceous theropod relatives. Also setting it apart is its camel-like humpback, which may have served to store body fat, control body temperature, attract a mate, or intimidate enemies.

A **Bakonydraco** pterosaur attacks a nest of **Ajkaceratops**

Known as the dragon of the Bakony Mountains in western Hungary, *Bakonydraco* was a flying reptile with a wingspan of eleven to thirteen feet. It is pictured here with *Ajkaceratops*, a horned ceratopsian dinosaur also of the Late Cretaceous period.

16

Dilong paradoxus in search of food

Like its larger descendant *Tyrannosuarus rex*, *Dilong paradoxus* had a strong jaw and sharp teeth for killing and eating its prey. Its species name, *paradoxus*, is a reference to its surprising covering of proto-feathers, which indicate that this small tyrannosaur may have been warm-blooded.

Giraffatitan and **Dicraeosaurus** sauropods grazing

Giraffatitan and *Dicraeosaurus* coexisted during the Late Jurassic period. Both had relatively long necks and tails, but these and other plant eaters varied widely in size. *Giraffatitan* evolved a long, slender neck that allowed it to feed at treetop level, more than thirty feet from the ground.

A **Neovenator** allosaur looms over a **Polacanthus**

Some 120 million years ago, *Neovenator* and *Polacanthus* were, respectively, carnivore and herbivore, predator and prey. *Neovenator*, at about 24 feet long, was much larger than *Polacanthus*, though the latter's armor may have been a defensive asset.

A meat-eating **Labocania** attacks
a young plant-eating **Magnapaulia**

With incredible jaw strength, a body built for speed, and an unusually large brain for a theropod, *Labocania* was likely a formidable hunter. *Magnapaulia*, a giant hadrosaur, would have had size on its side; its skeletal remains suggest body lengths of up to fifty feet, roughly twice that of *Labocania*.

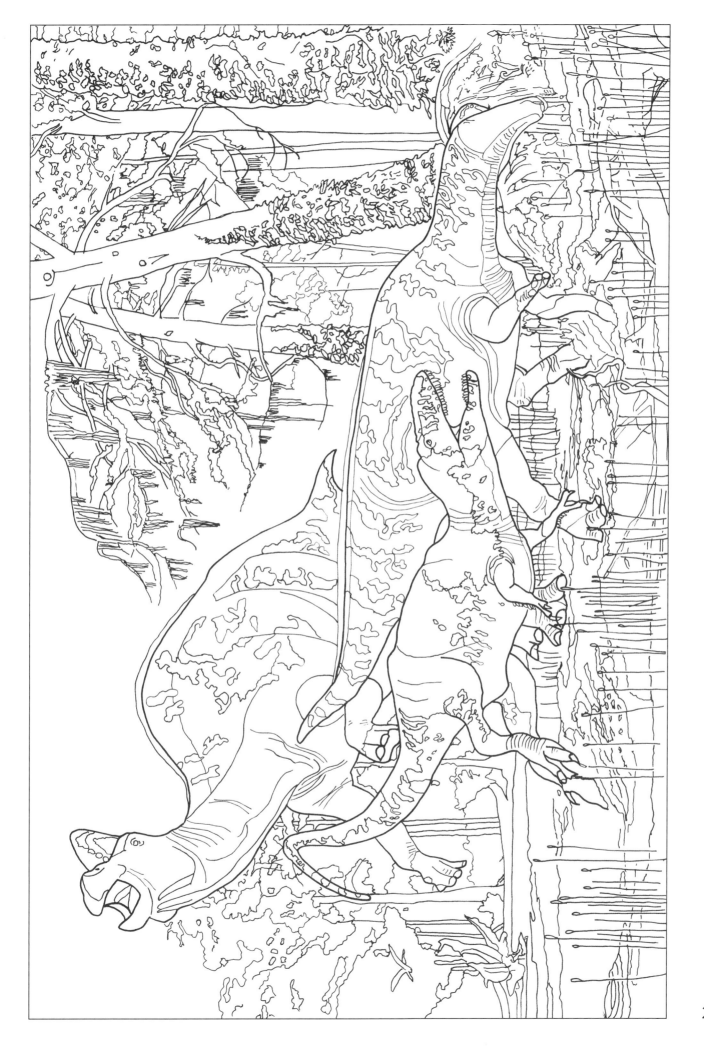

20

Two **Gigantspinosaurus** stegosaurs in sight of a large **Yangchuanosaurus** theropod

Biped carnivore *Yangchuanosaurus* was large and fierce. Quadruped herbivore *Gigantspinosaurus*, though smaller, was no slouch in the arms department, with two huge spikes jutting out from behind its shoulder blades as well as spikes along the length of its spine and on the tip of its tail.

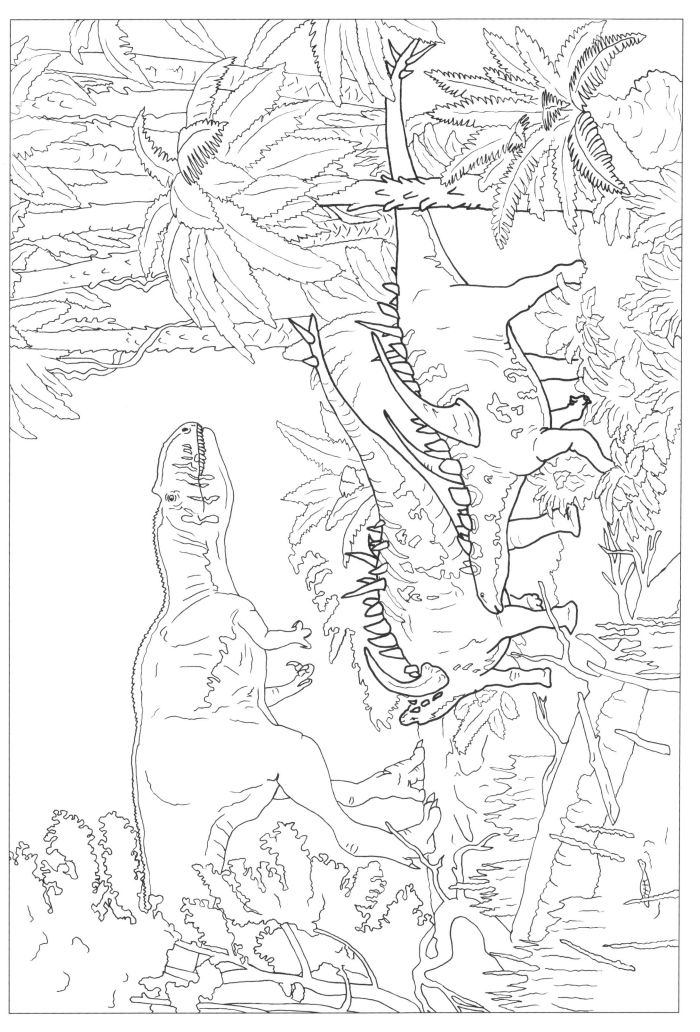

A **Saurolophus** hadrosaur rears up
beside a **Tarchia** ankylosaur

Saurolophus and *Tarchia* are known from complete or nearly complete skeletons. Study of post-hatchling hadrosaurs suggests that duck-billed *Saurolophus* may have developed its distinctive spike-like head crest later in life. *Tarchia* fossils reveal that its head and body were armored, and its tail end featured a bony club.